POWER BASICS+PLUS

Biology

Test Pack

WALCH PUBLISHING

1   2   3   4   5   6   7   8   9   10

ISBN 0-8251-5857-5

Copyright © 1998, 2001, 2005

J. Weston Walch, Publisher

P. O. Box 658 • Portland, Maine 04104-0658

walch.com

Printed in the United States of America

Table of Contents

© 2005 Walch Publishing
Biology Test Pack

To the Teacher

Power Basics® is a complete textbook program designed to meet the needs of students who are daunted by traditional textbooks. *Power Basics* was created with the teacher in mind, as well. The test pack for each student text in the *Power Basics* program includes straightforward, accurate, and easy-to-score assessment tools.

Each test pack includes

■ a pretest that covers all the material in the student text

■ a comprehensive test for every unit of the student text

■ a posttest for final testing and assessment after working through the entire student text

■ an answer key and testing guidance for both teacher and student

With testing a critical component of a school's curriculum today, students need to learn test-taking skills. This *Power Basics* test pack provides not only tests related to the student text, but special reference sections devoted to the topic of testing. "Testing Students Who Do Not Test Well" helps you give all your students the tools they need to be successful test-takers. "Test-Taking Strategies for *Power Basics*" and "Strategies for Standardized Testing" give students useful information about preparing for the tests in this test pack and for high-stakes standardized tests. These sections include key strategies for approaching tests with confidence. You may want to distribute and discuss these test-preparation tools before the pretest.

Finally, a handy record-keeping form permits you to track your students' progress as they work through the *Power Basics* student text.

Everything you need for test success is right here in *Power Basics*!

Testing Students Who Do Not Test Well

There are many reasons why some students do not test well. There may be language barriers, learning differences, or a failure to perceive the relevance or importance of a given assessment.

When working with a group of students who do not test well, it is important to identify the causes for the problems and, when possible, to find individual solutions for particular students.

Students who are easily distracted or who have been diagnosed with ADD or ADHD may benefit from taking the test in a quieter, more restrictive atmosphere. Give such students the option of taking a test during a break period, such as a study hall or lunch period. If possible, provide study carrels in your classroom to minimize external distractions.

Students with a low level of English proficiency will benefit from either having the instructions translated into their native language, having translation materials on their desks during the test, or having a translator present. Such students will invariably need more time than others to complete a test.

For students who see no benefit to a given test, discuss the purposes and benefits of testing in general with them ahead of time. There will be tests in every area of the student's life, from taking the test to become a licensed driver to getting into the college or trade school of his or her choice. Test-taking is an important skill, one that will serve students well throughout life.

The work you do with your students on test preparation will provide them with the tools they need to master not only the tests in this course, but the tests they will face throughout their educational experiences and careers.

Test-Taking Strategies for *Power Basics*®

Tests are a part of life. Whether you're facing a test in the classroom, a standardized test, or even a driver's test, there are tools you can use to help you be successful. The best way to do well on a test is to pay attention in class and study the material. But you can also prepare in other ways. Knowing how the test is set up can help you approach the test with confidence.

Tests come in many formats. They will vary in their structure. Some tests may contain only one question format, such as multiple choice. Others may have true/false, matching, fill-in-the-blank, short-answer, or essay questions. Some tests may ask you to read a passage and then answer questions about it. Others may ask you to refer to or make a graph or a chart. No matter what types of questions the test contains, using specific strategies for each question type can help you be successful.

The tests for the *Power Basics*® program often include multiple-choice questions. The following strategies can help you answer this type of question.

Multiple Choice

In multiple-choice questions, you read each question and choose the best answer out of two or more choices. These choices are usually labeled with the letters *a, b, c, d,* and *e,* depending on the number of choices. Use the following steps to help you answer multiple-choice questions.

- Read the directions very carefully. Some multiple-choice tests will ask you to select the *correct* answer, and others will ask you to select the *best* answer.

- Read the first part of the question very carefully. Look for negative words such as *not, never, except, unless,* and so forth.

- Answer each question in your mind before looking at the answer choices. Then read the answer choices before selecting an answer.

- After reading the choices, rule out the choices that are obviously incorrect. Then choose an answer from the remaining choices.

BIOLOGY • PRETEST

Circle the letter of the correct answer to each of the following questions.

1. What are lipids?

   a. sugars and starches

   b. the molecules that make up fats and oils

   c. proteins that are involved in chemical reactions in organisms

   d. the basic units of proteins

2. What is the largest, most visible structure in most cells?

   a. the Golgi complex

   b. the lysosomes

   c. the mitochondria

   d. the nucleus

3. How many pairs of chromosomes are found in the human cell?

   a. 7

   b. 19

   c. 23

   d. 27

4. In peas, green pea pods are dominant over yellow ones. If you cross a green homozygous variety with a yellow variety, what will the F_2 generation look like?

   a. all green

   b. all yellow

   c. half green and half yellow

   d. three quarters green and one quarter yellow

5. What is the most important characteristic of a species?

   a. Individuals must be able to interbreed and produce fertile offspring.

   b. Individuals must belong to the same population.

   c. Individuals must possess the same genotype.

   d. Individuals must possess the same phenotype.

6. What simple organisms live in extreme environments such as very salty water or the intestines of animals?

    a. protists

    b. archaebacteria

    c. algae

    d. fungi

7. Which of the following is one of the positive uses of bacteria?

    a. breaking down soil and making it fertile

    b. strengthening bones

    c. lowering cholesterol levels

    d. pasteurizing dairy products

8. What part of a fungus is usually seen above the ground?

    a. the mycelium

    b. the enzyme-producing structures

    c. the filaments

    d. the spore-bearing structures

9. Which of the following organelles are found in plants but not in animals?

    a. lysosomes

    b. nuclei

    c. mitochondria

    d. chloroplasts

10. What is the source of energy that fuels photosynthesis?

    a. sunlight

    b. anaerobic reactions

    c. decaying plant material

    d. geothermal power

11. What do the rings on the inside of a tree trunk represent?

   a. a healthy tree

   b. a diseased tree

   c. a year of nitrogen deficiency

   d. a year of secondary growth

12. Why do some flowering plants have colorful petals and produce nectar?

   a. to attract animals for pollination

   b. to protect them from being eaten

   c. to warn animals that they are dangerous

   d. to increase photosynthesis

13. What invertebrate phylum includes the sponges?

   a. poriferan

   b. cnidarian

   c. platyhelminthes

   d. nematodes

14. Which of the following is true of all mollusks?

   a. They live in the ocean.

   b. They have a muscular foot.

   c. They hunt their prey.

   d. They have a two-part shell.

15. What animals spend part of their lives in water and part on land?

   a. fish

   b. reptiles

   c. amphibians

   d. birds

16. What part of the circulatory system carries blood away from the heart?

    a. arteries

    b. capillaries

    c. lymph vessels

    d. veins

17. What is the term for organisms that invade larger organisms and cause disease?

    a. aliens

    b. antibodies

    c. hosts

    d. pathogens

18. What are vertebrae?

    a. bones that protect the brain

    b. bones that surround the nerve cord

    c. leg bones

    d. ribs

19. What part of the eye contains the light receptors known as rods and cones?

    a. cornea

    b. iris

    c. lens

    d. retina

20. What does the autonomic nervous system control?

    a. sensations we are aware of and involuntary muscle movements

    b. sensations we are aware of and voluntary muscle movements

    c. sensations we are not aware of and involuntary muscle movements

    d. sensations we are not aware of and voluntary muscle movements

21. What is the male sex hormone?

  a. estrogen

  b. follicle stimulating hormone

  c. luteinizing hormone

  d. testosterone

22. What is the niche of a species?

  a. its coloring

  b. its habitat and activity patterns

  c. its reproductive system

  d. its digestive tract

23. What is parasitism?

  a. a relationship in which one organism benefits and one suffers

  b. a relationship in which neither organism benefits

  c. a relationship in which both organisms benefit

  d. a relationship in which one organism benefits and the other is not affected

24. Why do some organisms mimic, or look like, others?

  a. to attract mates

  b. for protection

  c. to make hunting easier

  d. to take over another organism's territory

25. Which of the following biomes contains the largest number of plant species?

  a. taiga

  b. deserts

  c. grasslands

  d. tropical rain forests

UNIT 1 TEST • BUILDING BLOCKS OF LIVING THINGS

Circle the letter of the correct answer to each of the following questions.

1. When did life begin on Earth?
    a. 100 to 300 million years ago
    b. 1.5 to 2 billion years ago
    c. 3.5 to 4 billion years ago
    d. 10 to 12 billion years ago

2. Which of the following organelles is found only in plants?
    a. chloroplasts
    b. lysosomes
    c. mitochondria
    d. nucleus

3. What is the process by which plants get energy directly from the sun?
    a. electron transport chain
    b. glycosis
    c. Krebs cycle
    d. photosynthesis

4. What part of the cell controls what enters and leaves the cell?
    a. cell membrane
    b. cell wall
    c. cytoplasm
    d. flagella

5. What is the control center in a complex cell?
    a. cell wall
    b. lysosome
    c. mitochondria
    d. nucleus

6. What does the cell's DNA do?

    a. contains instructions for the proteins the cell should make

    b. controls what enters and leaves the cell

    c. helps the cell move around

    d. provides a rigid wall that gives the cell its shape

7. How do DNA strands wrap around each other?

    a. in a double helix

    b. in a double ring

    c. in interlocking ovals

    d. in a sphere

8. How many pairs of chromosomes does a normal human cell contain?

    a. 12

    b. 18

    c. 23

    d. 28

9. Which of the following represents chromosome pair number 23 for a male?

    a. XX

    b. XY

    c. YY

    d. none of the above

10. What is the term for an identical copy of a chromosome?

    a. centromere

    b. chromatid

    c. spindle

    d. Y chromosome

11. Who first deciphered the true patterns of heredity?

    a. Hippocrates

    b. Mendel

    c. Pasteur

    d. Weismann

12. Color blindness is a recessive, sex-linked trait. A color-blind man marries a color-blind woman. What are the chances that the children they expect to have will be color-blind?

    a. 100 percent for the girls and 50 percent for the boys

    b. 50 percent for the girls and 100 percent for the boys

    c. 50 percent for both sexes

    d. 100 percent for both sexes

13. What is the term for alleles that are neither dominant nor recessive?

    a. codominant

    b. corecessive

    c. mutually dominant

    d. mutually recessive

14. Which of the following genes would most quickly disappear from a population?

    a. dominant genes for a fatal disease

    b. recessive genes for a fatal disease

    c. dominant genes for a dangerous but not always fatal disease

    d. recessive genes for a dangerous but not always fatal disease

15. What is "fitness," as evolutionary biologists use the term?

    a. the ability to pass on genes to the next generation, relative to other individuals of the same species

    b. the ability to pass on genes to the next generation, relative to individuals of other species

    c. intelligence, relative to other individuals of the same species

    d. strength, relative to individuals of other species

16. What is a gene pool?

    a. the total amount of genotypes within a population

    b. the total amount of genotypes within a species

    c. the total amount of phenotypes within a population

    d. the total amount of phenotypes within a species

17. What is resource partitioning?

    a. competition among species for the same food

    b. competition among species for the same area

    c. specialization among species in the same area, so that they do not compete with one another

    d. specialization among species in different areas, so that they do not compete with one another

18. What is the usual order of the levels used in classifying organisms?

    a. species, phylum, class, order, family, kingdom, genus

    b. phylum, kingdom, class, species, order, family, genus

    c. kingdom, phylum, class, order, family, genus, species

    d. kingdom, species, phylum, class, order, family, genus

19. What two levels of classification are used to name an organism?

    a. genus and kingdom

    b. species and phylum

    c. order and genus

    d. genus and species

20. What animals will share the most genes?

    a. animals in the same class

    b. animals in the same family

    c. animals in the same order

    d. animals in the same phylum

UNIT 2 TEST • SIMPLE ORGANISMS

Circle the letter of the correct answer to each of the following questions.

1. What were probably the earliest life forms on Earth?

   a. algae

   b. bacteria

   c. diatoms

   d. viruses

2. What is the name for cells that do not have a nucleus?

   a. prokaryotic

   b. nuclear

   c. eukaryotic

   d. bacterial

3. How do most bacteria reproduce?

   a. by spores

   b. by seeds

   c. by diffusion

   d. by binary fission

4. Which of the following are the three most common eubacteria shapes?

   a. spiral, circle, and sphere

   b. spiral, rod, and sphere

   c. rod, rectangle, and circle

   d. sphere, spiral, and rectangle

5. Which of the following diseases is caused by bacteria?

   a. measles

   b. influenza

   c. botulism

   d. strep throat

6. What is an algal bloom?

    a. the flowering of certain water plants when exposed to algae

    b. the flowering tip of multicellular algae

    c. a rapid growth of algae

    d. a type of algae that lives on flowering water plants

7. What is red tide?

    a. an algal bloom of certain dinoflagellates that contain a red pigment

    b. an algal bloom of diatoms that contain a red pigment

    c. a kind of red algae that lives in snow

    d. a kind of red seaweed

8. What is the name for a protozoan that attaches itself to another organism and uses the host organism for food?

    a. ciliate

    b. dinoflagellate

    c. parasite

    d. pseudopod

9. What type of algae are commonly known as seaweed?

    a. blue-green algae

    b. brown algae

    c. green algae

    d. red algae

10. What is the name for the foot-like extension of cytoplasm some protozoans use to move?

    a. flagellum

    b. cilium

    c. pseudopod

    d. fingers

11. What makes single-celled protists different from bacteria?

    a. They have DNA.

    b. They have a nucleus.

    c. They have cell walls.

    d. They have flagella.

12. What do paramecia use to move?

    a. flagella

    b. pseudopods

    c. cilia

    d. fingers

13. What is a community of slime molds called?

    a. colony

    b. plasmodium

    c. sporangia

    d. algae

14. What is the basic structure in a fungus called?

    a. hypha

    b. mycelium

    c. spore

    d. yeast

15. What type of growth is actually an association between a fungus and algae?

    a. ameba

    b. lichen

    c. mycelium

    d. mushroom

16. How do fungi reproduce?

    a. through seeds

    b. through budding off

    c. through spores

    d. through eggs

17. What is one important role fungi play in the ecosystem?

    a. decomposers

    b. producers

    c. first-order consumers

    d. scavengers

18. What do fungi release into the organism they feed on in order to digest it?

    a. an acid

    b. an alkaline

    c. an enzyme

    d. a nutrient

19. Which of the following human conditions is caused by a fungus?

    a. polio

    b. athlete's foot

    c. malaria

    d. strep throat

20. Which of the following organisms is a fungus?

    a. ameba

    b. bacterium

    c. mushroom

    d. alga

UNIT 3 TEST • THE PLANT KINGDOM

Unit 3 Test • Biology Test Pack

Circle the letter of the correct answer to each of the following questions.

1. What is the complex sugar that makes up the cell walls of plants?
   a. cellulose
   b. sucrose
   c. fructose
   d. glucose

2. What is the name of the structures in plant cells that are filled with cell sap?
   a. chloroplasts
   b. ribosomes
   c. vacuoles
   d. mitochondria

3. Which of the following gases do plants give off during photosynthesis?
   a. carbon dioxide
   b. oxygen
   c. nitrogen
   d. hydrogen

4. What is the name of the simple sugar that is produced by photosynthesis?
   a. fructose
   b. glucose
   c. lactose
   d. sucrose

5. In what part of the plant does photosynthesis usually take place?
   a. roots
   b. flowers
   c. leaves
   d. stems

6. What type of root system consists of many stringy roots that cling to the soil?

    a. cap root system

    b. fibrous root system

    c. root hair system

    d. taproot system

7. What does the bacterium rhizobium help legumes use?

    a. carbon dioxide

    b. oxygen

    c. nitrogen

    d. phosphorus

8. What is the name of the system that carries water from a plant's roots to its leaves?

    a. reproductive system

    b. vascular system

    c. metabolic system

    d. storage system

9. How does water travel up the stem of a plant?

    a. It is pumped by cells in the roots.

    b. It is pumped by cells in the xylem tissue.

    c. It is pushed by water pressure in the soil.

    d. It is pulled upward by the evaporation process.

10. What is the name for the cells that carry sugars from the leaves to the rest of the plant?

    a. xylem

    b. phloem

    c. cambium

    d. chlorophyll

11. What is the name for the water-conducting tissue in plants?

    a. xylem

    b. phloem

    c. cambium

    d. chlorophyll

12. Why are most leaves flat and thin?

    a. to maximize exposure to light and maximize exposure to carbon dioxide

    b. to maximize exposure to light and minimize exposure to carbon dioxide

    c. to minimize exposure to light and minimize exposure to carbon dioxide

    d. to minimize exposure to light and maximize exposure to carbon dioxide

13. What do trees in temperate climates gain when they drop their leaves in the fall?

    a. They increase photosynthesis.

    b. They reduce the amount of energy they will need in the spring.

    c. They increase the amount of water their roots can draw in.

    d. They reduce water loss.

14. What is phototropism in plants a response to?

    a. soil

    b. gravity

    c. water

    d. light

15. Why do mosses remain small?

    a. They cannot absorb water.

    b. They cannot anchor themselves in the soil.

    c. They cannot photosynthesize.

    d. They have no way to distribute water and sugars throughout the entire plant.

16. What is the purpose of nectar?

    a. to attract animals

    b. to protect against diseases

    c. to regulate water loss

    d. to repel animals

17. What is the pistil of a flower?

    a. the female part of a flower

    b. a lobe that contains pollen

    c. the male part of a flower

    d. the part of the flower that produces nectar

18. What plant group includes pine trees?

    a. gymnosperms

    b. angiosperms

    c. ferns

    d. worts

19. What plant group includes most food plants?

    a. gymnosperms

    b. angiosperms

    c. ferns

    d. mosses

20. What is the name for a plant with two seed leaves?

    a. monocot

    b. spore

    c. dicot

    d. cone

UNIT 4 TEST • THE ANIMAL KINGDOM

Circle the letter of the correct answer to each of the following questions.

1. How do animals get energy?
    a. by photosynthesis
    b. by consuming other organisms
    c. by decomposing other organisms
    d. through a symbiotic relationship with other organisms

2. Why do tapeworms not need a digestive tract?
    a. because they get energy by photosynthesis
    b. because their food has already been digested by the host
    c. because they only eat simple sugars
    d. because they eat grass and leaves

3. Which of the following types of worms have a closed circulatory system?
    a. annelids
    b. flukes
    c. nematodes
    d. tapeworms

4. Which of the following types of worms cause trichinosis?
    a. annelids
    b. flukes
    c. nematodes
    d. tapeworms

5. What phylum are arachnids classed in?
    a. arthropods
    b. mollusks
    c. annelids
    d. platyhelminthes

6. What happens to arthropods during molting?

    a. They are born.

    b. They reproduce.

    c. They shed their coats in order to grow.

    d. They die in order to create a new generation.

7. What are the three major classes of mollusks?

    a. pseudopods, gastropods, and bivalves

    b. gastropods, pseudopods, and cephalopods

    c. gastropods, bivalves, and cephalopods

    d. pseudopods, cephalopods, and bivalves

8. To which class do snails and slugs belong?

    a. cephalopods

    b. bivalves

    c. gastropods

    d. pseudopods

9. How many legs do arachnids have?

    a. two

    b. four

    c. six

    d. eight

10. How do insects take in oxygen?

    a. through gills, which feed the oxygen into the circulatory system

    b. through lungs, which feed the oxygen into the circulatory system

    c. through the mouth, which takes the oxygen directly to the cells

    d. through tubes called trachea, which take the oxygen directly to the cells

11. How many legs do insects have?

    a. two

    b. four

    c. six

    d. eight

12. The bodies of insects are divided into how many main sections?

    a. one

    b. two

    c. three

    d. four

13. What does the swim bladder of bony fish allow them to do?

    a. breathe underwater

    b. dive more quickly

    c. float at various depths

    d. maneuver more quickly

14. What is the skeleton of a shark made of?

    a. bone

    b. cartilage

    c. chiton

    d. silica

15. How do most fish reproduce?

    a. binary fission

    b. laying eggs

    c. budding off

    d. producing spores

16. What were the first new land animals to evolve from the fish that came to live on dry land?

    a. amphibians

    b. insects

    c. mammals

    d. reptiles

17. Why do amphibians need to return to the water?

    a. to breathe

    b. to feed

    c. to sleep

    d. to reproduce

18. In what ways are reptiles similar to amphibians?

    a. Both breathe through their skin.

    b. Both can expand their ribcages to expand their lungs.

    c. Both have lungs.

    d. Both must live in moist climates.

19. Birds directly evolved from what other animals?

    a. amphibians

    b. fish

    c. mammals

    d. reptiles

20. What are placental mammals?

    a. cold-blooded mammals

    b. mammals that complete their development in a pouch attached to the mother's body

    c. mammals that complete their development inside the mother's uterus

    d. mammals that lay eggs

UNIT 5 TEST • THE HUMAN BODY

Circle the letter of the correct answer to each of the following questions.

1. How long is the typical human digestive tract?

    a. less than 1 meter

    b. about 3 meters

    c. over 9 meters

    d. over 13 meters

2. What are the chemicals that break down food into the four basic organic compounds?

    a. carbohydrates

    b. enzymes

    c. hormones

    d. lipids

3. Urine is finally expelled from the body through which of the following organs?

    a. bladder

    b. collecting duct

    c. kidneys

    d. urethra

4. What does the hemoglobin in red blood cells do?

    a. It binds carbon dioxide.

    b. It binds oxygen.

    c. It releases antibodies.

    d. It releases carbon dioxide.

5. What chamber of the heart pumps blood into the pulmonary artery, which leads to the lungs?

    a. the left atrium

    b. the left ventricle

    c. the right atrium

    d. the right ventricle

6. In which part of the circulatory system is blood brought directly to the tissues?

    a. in the arteries

    b. in the arterioles

    c. in the capillaries

    d. in the veins

7. When a cell first takes in a virus, what organelle tries to destroy it?

    a. glycoprotein

    b. lysosome

    c. mitochondria

    d. nucleus

8. What type of cell engulfs an invading pathogen and displays its antigens?

    a. a lymphocyte

    b. a macrophage

    c. a red blood cell

    d. a platelet

9. What is keratin?

    a. an enzyme that attacks viruses

    b. a hormone that triggers immune responses

    c. a protein that surrounds a virus

    d. a waterproof protein that coats the top layer of skin

10. What is the principal component of the thickest layer of the skin?

    a. collagen

    b. elastin

    c. mast cells

    d. phagocytes

11. What is the tough protein that is one of the primary components of bones?

    a. collagen

    b. fibrinogen

    c. peptin

    d. periosteum

12. How many bones are contained in the adult body?

    a. 79

    b. 153

    c. 206

    d. 273

13. Which of the following bones protect the spinal cord?

    a. the femur

    b. the ribs

    c. the sternum

    d. the vertebrae

14. Which of the following types of muscles are voluntary?

    a. cardiac muscles

    b. skeletal muscles

    c. smooth muscles

    d. all of the above

15. What is the role of the proteins actin and myosin?

    a. attaching bones to bones

    b. attaching muscles to bone

    c. contracting the muscles

    d. storing energy

16. Where is insulin produced?

    a. in the hypothalamus

    b. in the liver

    c. in the pancreas

    d. in the thyroid

17. Which of the following receptors respond best to dim light?

    a. blue-sensitive cones

    b. green-sensitive cones

    c. red-sensitive cones

    d. rods

18. What is the hormone that causes secondary characteristics in males?

    a. adrenaline

    b. estrogen

    c. progesterone

    d. testosterone

19. Where are eggs produced in the female body?

    a. in the oviduct

    b. in the ovaries

    c. in the uterus

    d. in the vagina

20. During pregnancy, why is it especially important that the mother eats properly and avoids alcohol and drugs?

    a. because the embryo's kidneys are already functioning

    b. because the placenta allows some toxins to reach the embryo

    c. because the placenta rejects all toxins

    d. because toxins can rupture the umbilical cord

UNIT 6 TEST • ECOLOGY

Circle the letter of the correct answer to each of the following questions.

1. According to the food pyramid, in a given area, which group will have the second largest number of members?
   a. producers
   b. primary consumers
   c. secondary consumers
   d. tertiary consumers

2. Where do plants that photosynthesize get the carbon they need?
   a. from bacteria
   b. from carbon dioxide in the atmosphere
   c. from water
   d. through nitrogen fixation

3. Why is the loss of forests in Central America harming cherry trees in the United States?
   a. because birds that eat tent caterpillars have lost their winter habitat
   b. because cherry trees are now being cut to take the place of tropical woods
   c. because insect pests are now coming north
   d. because oxygen is declining in the atmosphere

4. After a plant absorbs energy from the sun, which part(s) of that energy will be available to an animal that eats the plant?
   a. the energy used in growing
   b. the energy used in reproduction
   c. the energy stored in sugars
   d. all of the above

5. A lake in New Hampshire is filling up with sediment. What will be its final stage of succession?
   a. a bog
   b. grassland
   c. a forest of quick-growing trees
   d. a forest of shade-tolerant trees

6. A plowed field has been abandoned. What are the first plants that will take over?

   a. deciduous trees

   b. grasses

   c. pines

   d. shrubs

7. For which resource is competition among plants the most intense?

   a. light

   b. nutrients

   c. space

   d. water

8. What is the term for an association between organisms in which both organisms benefit?

   a. a parasitic relationship

   b. a strategic relationship

   c. a symbiotic relationship

   d. a synergistic relationship

9. Why is it an advantage for other snakes to mimic the coral snake?

   a. because the coral snake is a deadly constrictor

   b. because the coral snake is inconspicuous

   c. because the coral snake is very fast

   d. because the coral snake is very poisonous

10. What happens when monarch caterpillars eat milkweed?

    a. They die.

    b. They mimic the shape of the plant.

    c. The plant's poison remains in their bodies, making them distasteful to predators.

    d. They take on the plant's color, camouflaging them from predators.

11. Which of the following predators is the fastest?

  a. the cheetah

  b. the leopard

  c. the lion

  d. the wolf

12. Which of the following is an example of mutualism?

  a. the relationship between the honey guide and the honey badger

  b. the relationship between a tapeworm and its host

  c. the relationship between a shark and the fish that eat its leavings

  d. the relationship between a rhinoceros and the birds that eat insects off its back

13. How much rain typically falls on the tundra?

  a. very little

  b. a moderate amount

  c. a moderate to heavy amount

  d. a heavy amount

14. What biome usually receives the most precipitation?

  a. deciduous forest

  b. desert

  c. tropical rain forest

  d. grasslands

15. What are epiphytes?

  a. animals that live in trees

  b. insect parasites that prey on trees

  c. plant parasites that prey on trees

  d. plants that grow in trees instead of in the soil

16. What biome is the home for many of the world's fastest animals?

 a. boreal forest

 b. desert

 c. grassland

 d. tropical rain forest

17. How are most grasses pollinated?

 a. by insects

 b. by birds

 c. by the wind

 d. by mammals

18. What is permafrost?

 a. the layer of ground in the tundra that remains frozen throughout the year

 b. the layer of ground in the tundra that thaws in warm weather

 c. the least severe frosts, which permanent residents of the tundra can survive

 d. the most severe frosts in the depth of winter

19. Where do most plants grow in the tropical rain forest?

 a. along streams

 b. in marshes

 c. in the tops of trees

 d. on dry ground

20. What does it mean to say that grasses recover easily from herbivory?

 a. They can easily repel animals that try to eat them.

 b. They grow back easily after being eaten by animals.

 c. They recover easily after being burned in fires.

 d. They resist plant diseases that are spread by grazing animals.

BIOLOGY • POSTTEST

Circle the letter of the correct answer to each of the following questions.

1. What are enzymes?

   a. sugars and starches

   b. the molecules that make up fats and oils

   c. proteins that are involved in chemical reactions in organisms

   d. the basic units of proteins

2. Which of the following is true about the nucleus?

   a. It starts and controls cell division.

   b. It is surrounded by the nucleolus.

   c. It processes glucose.

   d. It is the site of protein synthesis.

3. What is the term for a region of DNA that codes for a single protein or group of proteins?

   a. a gene

   b. a nitrogen base

   c. a nucleotide

   d. RNA

4. What is the term for traits that are governed by more than one gene?

   a. codominant traits

   b. dominant traits

   c. polygenic traits

   d. recessive traits

5. Which of the following situations will likely lead to speciation?

   a. Individuals from one population breed with individuals from a second population.

   b. Two populations occupy the same habitat type.

   c. Two populations are physically separated from each other.

   d. Members of the same population develop different color patterns.

6. What do prokaryotic cells lack?

   a. a membrane

   b. a cell wall

   c. cytoplasm

   d. a nucleus

7. Which of the following diseases is caused by bacteria?

   a. Lyme disease

   b. high blood pressure

   c. giardia

   d. Creutzfeldt-Jakob disease

8. Which of the following is one of the positive uses of fungi?

   a. causing Dutch elm disease

   b. making bread rise

   c. making yogurt

   d. cleaning the air

9. What are plant cell walls principally made of ?

   a. cellulose

   b. DNA

   c. muscle

   d. protein

10. Why do leaves of deciduous trees change color in the fall?

   a. The chlorophyll breaks down, and other pigments become visible that have been masked before.

   b. The chlorophyll changes color.

   c. New pigments develop in the late summer.

   d. New pigments move into the leaves from the stem.

11. What are the openings on the surface of a leaf called?

    a. xylem

    b. phloem

    c. stomata

    d. cambium

12. How do ferns reproduce?

    a. by cuttings

    b. by spores

    c. by budding off

    d. by seeds

13. Which invertebrate phylum includes jellyfish?

    a. poriferan

    b. cnidarian

    c. platyhelminthes

    d. nematodes

14. Which of the following is true of all fish?

    a. Their skeletons are made of cartilage.

    b. They use a swim bladder to float at any depth.

    c. They are cold-blooded.

    d. They live in salt water.

15. What is metamorphosis?

    a. a change in an animal's form

    b. the process of shedding the outer skin as an animal grows

    c. the reproductive process

    d. how animals get energy from food

16. Which of the following animals are reptiles?

    a. tortoises

    b. octopuses

    c. spiders

    d. marsupials

17. What is the function of enzymes in the digestive process?

    a. to break down food

    b. to destroy germs in food

    c. to move food through the digestive system

    d. to protect the stomach lining from acid

18. How do antibodies fight viruses?

    a. by altering their nucleic acids

    b. by coating them and preventing them from binding to host cells

    c. by digesting them

    d. by expelling them from the body

19. What is the term for the cords that attach muscles to bones?

    a. muscle fibers

    b. sinews

    c. striations

    d. tendons

20. Which vitamin does human skin synthesize?

    a. vitamin A

    b. vitamin D

    c. vitamin E

    d. vitamin K

21. What part of the eye regulates the amount of light that can enter?

   a. cornea

   b. iris

   c. lens

   d. retina

22. What hormone produces female sexual characteristics?

   a. estrogen

   b. follicle stimulating hormone

   c. progesterone

   d. testosterone

23. What are herbivores?

   a. animals that eat other animals

   b. animals that eat plants

   c. plants that poison animals

   d. plants that are parasitic on other plants

24. What is commensalism?

   a. a relationship in which one organism benefits and one suffers

   b. a relationship in which neither organism benefits

   c. a relationship in which both organisms benefit

   d. a relationship in which one organism benefits and the other is not affected

25. Which biome gets the most rainfall?

   a. taiga

   b. deserts

   c. tropical rain forests

   d. grasslands

Answer Key

Pretest

1. b	10. a	19. d
2. d	11. d	20. c
3. c	12. a	21. c
4. d	13. a	22. b
5. a	14. b	23. a
6. b	15. c	24. b
7. a	16. a	25. d
8. d	17. d	
9. d	18. b	

Unit 1 Test: Building Blocks of Living Things

1. c	8. c	15. a
2. a	9. b	16. a
3. d	10. b	17. c
4. a	11. b	18. c
5. d	12. d	19. d
6. a	13. a	20. b
7. a	14. a	

Unit 2 Test: Simple Organisms

1. b	8. c	15. b
2. a	9. b	16. c
3. d	10. c	17. a
4. b	11. b	18. c
5. d	12. c	19. b
6. c	13. b	20. c
7. a	14. a	

Unit 3 Test: The Plant Kingdom

1. a	8. b	15. d
2. c	9. d	16. a
3. b	10. b	17. a
4. b	11. a	18. a
5. c	12. a	19. b
6. b	13. d	20. c
7. c	14. d	

Unit 4 Test: The Animal Kingdom

1. b	8. c	15. b
2. b	9. d	16. a
3. a	10. d	17. d
4. c	11. c	18. c
5. a	12. c	19. d
6. c	13. c	20. c
7. c	14. b	

Unit 5 Test: The Human Body

1. c	8. b	15. c
2. b	9. d	16. c
3. d	10. a	17. d
4. b	11. a	18. d
5. d	12. c	19. b
6. c	13. d	20. b
7. b	14. b	

Unit 6 Test: Ecology

1. b	8. c	15. d
2. b	9. d	16. c
3. a	10. c	17. c
4. c	11. a	18. a
5. d	12. a	19. c
6. b	13. a	20. b
7. a	14. c	

Posttest

1. c	10. a	19. d
2. a	11. c	20. b
3. a	12. b	21. b
4. c	13. b	22. a
5. c	14. c	23. b
6. d	15. a	24. d
7. a	16. a	25. c
8. b	17. a	
9. a	18. b	

Student Record-Keeping Form

Student Name	Student ID	Class Period	Pretest Score	Unit ___ Score	Unit ___ Score	Unit ___ Score	Unit ___ Score	Unit ___ Score	Unit ___ Score	Unit ___ Score	Posttest Score
1.											
2.											
3.											
4.											
5.											
6.											
7.											
8.											
9.											
10.											
11.											
12.											
13.											
14.											
15.											
16.											
17.											
18.											
19.											
20.											
21.											
22.											
23.											
24.											
25.											
26.											
27.											
28.											
29.											
30.											

Strategies for Standardized Testing

Every other year or so, depending on your state, you are required to take a standardized test. The purpose of standardized tests is to let your state know how well you and other students in your school perform on academic subjects the state and federal government believe you should know in your grade. Taking a standardized test, and doing well on it, is a skill that can be acquired and perfected, like any other skill. This section will provide you with tips and strategies you need to learn to take tests well.

The person giving the test, usually your teacher, will do everything he or she can to make you more comfortable during the test. Even so, you probably already know that the tests can be a little stressful. They last a long time, and each section is timed. You are not allowed to get out of your chair during the period of the test. However, there are ways to minimize the stress, at least when it comes to answering the questions themselves.

Know what to expect.

Standardized tests usually have four different kinds of questions on the science portion of the tests. State tests differ, but you should prepare for all four kinds of questions. The simplest kind is multiple choice. In multiple choice, you read the question and choose the best answer out of four, or sometimes five, choices.

The next type of question is called a constructed-response, or a short-answer question. A constructed-response question requires you to write a short answer of one or two words or a simple sentence in response to a question. It may also be a fill-in-the-blank type of question. It may ask you to make a graph or a chart.

The third type of question asks you to write an essay. For an essay question, you will write a paragraph or two in response to a question.

The last type, which is only used in science tests, is called short lab. With this kind of question, you will be given equipment and told how to perform a short experiment. After the experiment, you will answer questions.

You may also be given the opportunity to do pretests, or practice tests. They will help you to get an idea of what the real test will be like. The samples will also give you clues about what kinds of content will be on the actual test.

Look at the expected answers once you get the practice tests back. Your wrong answers, especially, will help you figure out how the graders of the real test will mark answers.

By doing practice tests, you will also be familiar with the kinds of questions that may be asked and the form in which they may be asked.

Strategies for Standardized Testing, *cont.*

It's your test; organize it the way you want.

Unless you are specifically told otherwise, within each testing period, there is no rule that says you must answer the questions in the order they appear. You might choose to answer all the multiple-choice questions first, followed by the constructed-response questions, and save the essay question for last. (Short labs are usually done in their own testing period.) Or, you might answer the questions you are relatively sure about first, then go back to the things about which you are unsure.

How you organize your test is up to you, but it is best to give it a little thought before you take the test. By taking the practice tests, you can figure out ahead of time what strategy works well for you.

Eliminate obviously wrong answers first.

Especially in multiple-choice questions, there are often answers that you know, or feel strongly, are wrong. You can often get rid of one or two wrong answers quickly. For instance, read the following multiple-choice question:

Question: Why does the Northern Hemisphere experience summer?

a. Earth is closer to the Sun during the summer.

b. Earth is closer to the Sun during the winter.

c. The Northern Hemisphere does not experience seasons.

d. Earth is tilted, and more of the Sun's energy falls directly on the Northern Hemisphere during the summer.

In this question, you can easily eliminate choice *c*, because you know the Northern Hemisphere does in fact experience seasons. The answer seems to be either *a, b,* or *d.* Choice *b* is a correct statement.

Strategies for Standardized Testing, *cont.*

If you think about choices *a* and *b,* however, you will realize that neither one is the correct answer. Choice *b* is a correct statement (which means that choice *a* is an incorrect statement), but choice *b* doesn't correctly answer the question. If being close to the Sun caused summer, both the Northern and the Southern Hemispheres would experience summer at the same time, and they do not. Therefore, the best choice is *d.*

Even if you do not know the answer, you can often come up with a rational guess. Most tests mark unanswered questions wrong, so you cannot lose by making your best guess.

The foundation for success on your test is the content you learn in your classroom. Using some basic strategies and doing practice tests will also help you get ready for test time. Follow the formula for success below, and you can be confident that you'll do your best on test day.

| classroom knowledge | + | strategic insight | + | practice | = | SUCCESS |

Strategies for Standardized Testing, *cont.*

Here are some additional hints to help you succeed on any standardized test.

Helpful Hints

1. Listen carefully to all instructions from the person giving the test.

2. Read directions carefully. Be sure you understand all the directions before beginning that section of the test.

3. Read each question carefully. Then read all the answer choices before you answer the question.

4. If it's taking you a lot of time to answer one question, move on to the next one. If you take too much time on one question, you may not have a chance to get through the whole test. Answer the questions you know first. Then go back to the others if you have time.

5. Be sure to mark your answers on the answer sheet that comes with the test booklet. You will probably be asked to shade the circle that contains the letter of your answer.

6. Take care when marking your answer sheet. Check to make sure that the number on the answer sheet matches the number of the question you are answering.

7. Since most standardized tests are scored by a machine, mark your answer clearly and darkly. Make sure you mark only one answer for each question.

8. If you have time, go back and check your answers.